OUR BUILT ENVIRONMENT

WITHDRAWN

DESIGN AND TECHNOLOGY

interactions

STARTING POINT

LESLEY HEHIR AND JOAN KEAN

PROJECT CONSULTANT
Tristram Shepard

Stanley Thornes (Publishers) Ltd.

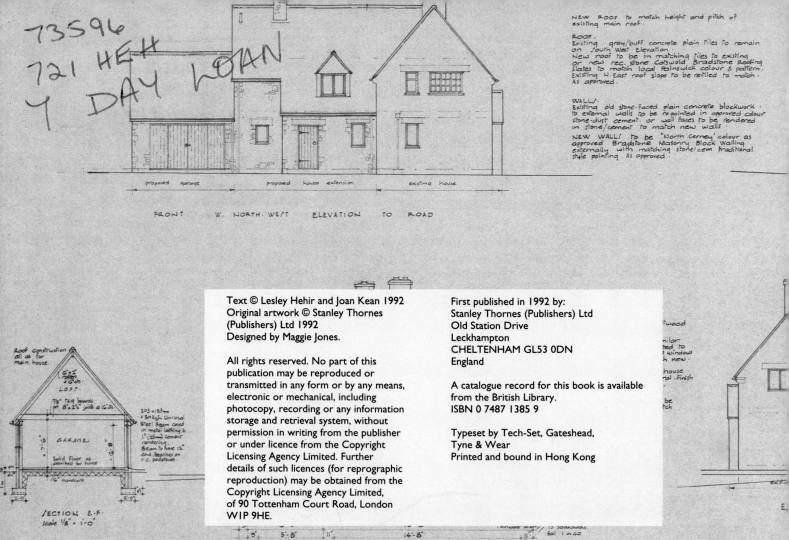

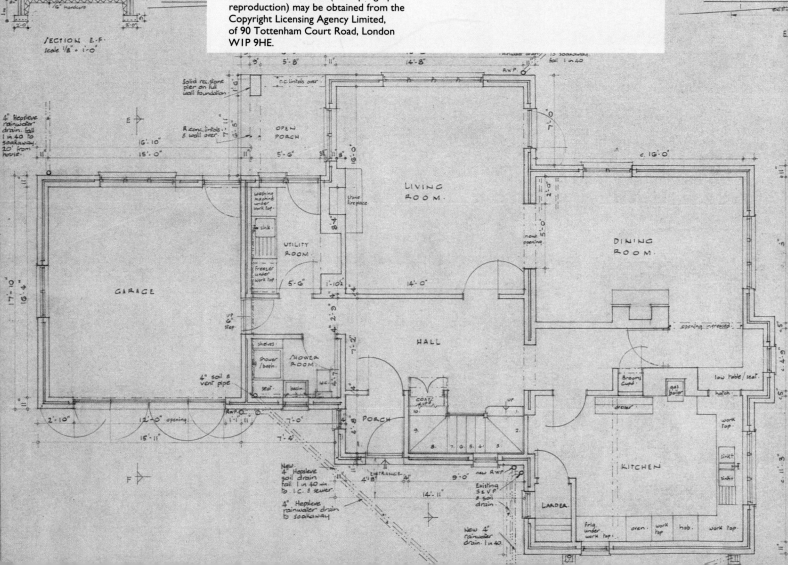

Text © Lesley Hehir and Joan Kean 1992
Original artwork © Stanley Thornes
(Publishers) Ltd 1992
Designed by Maggie Jones.

First published in 1992 by:
Stanley Thornes (Publishers) Ltd
Old Station Drive
Leckhampton
CHELTENHAM GL53 0DN
England

A catalogue record for this book is available
from the British Library.
ISBN 0 7487 1385 9

Typeset by Tech-Set, Gateshead,
Tyne & Wear
Printed and bound in Hong Kong

Contents

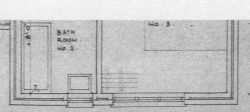

BUILDINGS *and* SPACES

For most of us, our everyday lives are lived in a built environment.

These are the surroundings where we carry out our daily activities. What do we mean by the built environment? Is it the architecture? What about the spaces between the buildings and the roads? All these elements are part of the built environment. Large concentrations of buildings and spaces form towns and cities. Smaller groups make up villages and hamlets.

Our villages, towns and cities have grown up over centuries. They are constantly changing, never finally designed or completed. What we see today is the result of changes in style and fashion, in building materials, in technology and in people's needs and activities.

The built environment has been planned and designed, shaped by people like builders and craftsmen as well as planners, architects and engineers.

Also responsible are the financiers and developers, without whose money little would be built today. There are also those who make decisions at government and local council level.

Imagine the town as one large building with lots of rooms, and the roads and streets as corridors. We spend most of our lives in and around this complex building – it is where we live, work and play. Towns and cities should give us a choice about where and how we live, work and play. Does it meet all our needs? How convenient, safe and comfortable is it? How easy is it to move around? How long will it last? Have the best materials and structures for the job been used? Is it pleasing to look at and use?

Think of the spaces between buildings as outdoor rooms with walls and floors. The shapes, colours, textures and patterns of the space and its street furniture all affect the way we feel. They all help create a particular atmosphere.

In this book we ask you to think about people's activities and the places and spaces they use. Consider how this built environment works, and why and how it has changed. How has it been designed, built and managed? How do the pieces fit together? We ask you to speculate on how the built environment will look in the future. As you work through the book you will need to think about the pictures and text carefully. Discuss together the questions and points raised. Try out some of the suggested activities. They will help you to understand the need for design and technology in the built environment and the opportunities it provides.

The TOWNSCAPE

What makes a place special? What make one place different from another?

When we describe a building we refer to its *architecture*. It is different with a collection of buildings. When we describe the relationships between buildings and the spaces between them, and to ourselves as we move around them, we refer to the 'townscape'.

We use all our senses in experiencing places - sight, touch, taste, smell and hearing.

Movement

Usually when we experience the built environment we are moving through it: on foot, bicycle, or in vehicles. As we move about, we see things differently.

Look at the sequence of four sketches of a prominent landmark in a city centre. They have been drawn at four different points on a journey towards it. What do you notice about the shape of the landmark and its size?

Choose a prominent feature in the built environment near you. Move towards it and stop four times on your journey. At each stopping point spend about five minutes recording the shape of the feature and the space between yourself and it. Do not worry about the detail; concentrate on the shapes you see.

From your four sketches, choose the view that you like the most and the one you like the least. Explain your choices and the reasons for them to a friend.

In groups, look at the street scene above. Each imagine you are one of the characters in the street. Where have you been? Where are you going to? Listen to the noises. Try to describe them either by using drawings or words.

Describe some of the smells. Which ones are pleasant and which are unpleasant?

Think of a place that is special to you. Close your eyes and imagine you are there. Describe what you imagine you can see, hear, smell, touch and taste.

Colour

Life would be boring in black and white. Think of three areas in your daily life in which colour plays an important part. When the neighbourhood of Byker in Newcastle was planned in the 1970s, a lot of thought was given to colour. Each individual neighbourhood can be identified by its particular colour on houses, fences and balconies.

What makes up the colour in our towns and cities? What occurs naturally, and what is added?

Look around your neighbourhood for examples of natural and applied colours.

Patterns and textures

You will find different textures on both walls and floors. See how many different surface textures you and your friends can find. Take rubbings with wax crayons on paper.

How do the surfaces you discovered change under different conditions? For example, how do they look and feel in sunlight and shadow, or after it has rained? Which of the floorscapes are easiest to walk on, which the hardest? How well can you walk, cycle or drive on them?

textures   materials   patterns   shapes   decoration

Scale and relationship

Which are big buildings and which are small buildings in this photograph? How did you decide?

You probably picked the largest building (the cathedral) and compared the other buildings to it. This relationship of sizes is known as 'scale'. Scale is the word used in comparing sizes of buildings, areas, distances and details of buildings.

You knew from experience that cathedrals are large. Public buildings often have their importance emphasised by being larger in scale than other buildings. The people in the photograph also helped you in making your decision. They give it 'human scale'. Imagine how you would feel if you were one of the people in the photograph. How would you feel in relation to the cathedral? How in relation to the space surrounded by the buildings?

Sometimes the scale of buildings, structures and spaces next to each are very dissimilar. This can produce unsettling and unpleasant visual effects.

friendly   threatening   illusory   mysterious   imposing   daunting   challenging   surprising   exaggerated   intimate

Look around the place in which you live for effects of scale. See which of the words on this list you could use in describing the examples you find. Which effects do you like and which do you dislike?

A sense of PLACE

What do we look at when we try to judge the quality of a townscape?

What are your opinions about the design of the newer buildings in the row on the right? Do you think they fit well into the older terrace? Are they harmonious?

Line, shape and form

Look at the roofline, and the shape and form of this 'infill' design. The shape is the two-dimensional aspect. The form is the three-dimensional aspect. Notice the scale and proportion of the windows and doors.

Trace over this drawing leaving the infill area blank. Draw in your own infill development, being aware of:

■ Scale
■ Line
■ Relationship
■ Form
■ Shape.

Is there anything else you should think about?

Go out into your area and look for infill developments. How do you feel about them? Are they good or bad? What makes you think so?

Critical appraisal

We can all have an opinion about a place. We may like it or not. It depends on several things: the way the different bits have been put together, or whether we had a good time there. Maybe friends or relatives live there; perhaps, simply, it is home. The important thing is to know what you like, what you do not like, and why.

This is Jane's 'appraisal' or 'assessment' sheet of an area in her town.

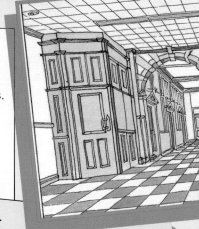

In pairs, read the words on the sheet. Decide how Jane has used the sheet and what her opinions of the area are. Do you both agree on the meanings of the words? In which areas in your neighbourhood

would you use such a sheet? Would you use these words or would you choose different ones?

Design your own appraisal sheet and use it in an area of your choice.

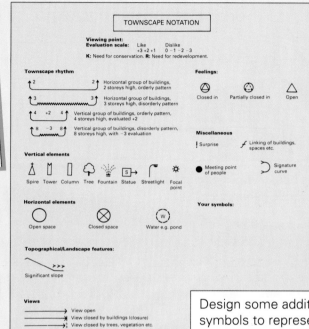

... are examples of ... an designer's ... nse to a street ... e and an ... tect's response to ... m. Comments have ... added. These ... ments or ... notations are not just ... ual, they also ... ress opinions.

This is the key to a series of symbols devised by Gordon Cullen as a sort of shorthand for noting down personal responses to the built environment. He called these symbols 'notation'. This time, choose the notation symbol which best describes the sketches below.

TOWNSCAPE NOTATION

Viewing point:
Evaluation scale: Like   Dislike
                +3 +2 +1   0 −1 −2 −3
K: Need for conservation. R: Need for redevelopment.

Townscape rhythm

     Horizontal group of buildings, 2 storeys high, orderly pattern
     Horizontal group of buildings, 3 storeys high, disorderly pattern
     Vertical group of buildings, orderly pattern, 4 storeys high, evaluated +2
     Vertical group of buildings, disorderly pattern, 8 storeys high, with −3 evaluation

Feelings:
Closed in   Partially closed in   Open

Vertical elements
Spire   Tower   Column   Tree   Fountain   Statue   Streetlight   Focal point

Miscellaneous
! Surprise   Linking of buildings, spaces etc.
● Meeting point of people   Signature curve

Horizontal elements
Open space   Closed space   Water e.g. pond

Your symbols:

Topographical/Landscape features:
Significant slope

Views
View open
View closed by buildings (closure)
View closed by trees, vegetation etc.
View screened by trees, columns etc.
View closed at lower level (1st storey) but distant view of trees can be seen above building.
View through arch   View between gap   Glimpse

* Approach through dingy lobbies
* Lacks central focus
* Lacks seating, fittings and furniture
* No visual guide to direction within the building
* Decoration and floorscape make for institutional atmosphere
* Fluorescent lighting out of character
* Vinyl tiling unstable
* Views from central hall uneven and disappointing

Imagine you were in these two places. Do you agree or disagree with the comments?

Take a photograph or make a sketch of a room or a street. Annotate it with your comments. Ask someone else to annotate the same scene. Discuss your views with each other.

Look at these six sketches and the list of words. For each sketch, choose the word that you think best describes the piece of townscape shown.

Design some additional symbols to represent elements you think are important in the environment.

Collect postcards and photographs of different built environments and 'notate' them using Gordon Cullen's and your own symbols. Take the drawings you have done of a landmark in your area and 'notate' them.

focal point

enclosure

change of level

surprise

space

visual block

The shape of things

Architecture and design go hand in hand with mechanics and physics.

This house was modelled and built in simple geometrical solids.

The shape of most buildings is based on simple solids such as cubes, boxes or cylinders. The most common is the box or group of boxes. Starting from a simple box structure, architects can cut, pierce and combine the boxes into different designs.

Towns and cities change in appearance largely because of changes in construction methods and materials.

Some architects deliberately set out to design a building which reminds us of something else. Sydney Opera House, set in the harbour, is meant to remind us of the billowing sails of boats.

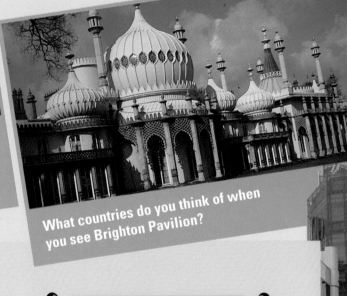

What countries do you think of when you see Brighton Pavilion?

Physical forces

Many forces act on a building. For example:

- The weight of the construction materials
- The weather
- People moving around in them
- Earth movements
- Heavy objects such as furniture.

A building must be stable, and not fall down. The design of the building therefore has to balance all such forces. To counteract the weight of a person walking across a room, the floor beams must push back with an equal force.

The materials used in building have to be strong in one of two ways. They may be strong when forces are pushing the material together, or compressing it. Or their strength may be seen when forces are pulling them apart, that is, when the material is in tension.

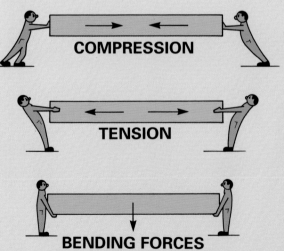

COMPRESSION

TENSION

BENDING FORCES

Try to devise some new shapes for buildings. Think of shapes from nature: sea shells, trees, flowers, leaves, spider's webs. Use one of these shapes as the basis for a building. Start with some quick sketches, and then make a model. You can use paper, card and glue but you may need straws or wooden splints to make the structure stand up.

The shape of a building often gives a clue about how it is constructed.

The construction method of building on a frame has been used from medieval to modern times. More recent framed buildings are in tension, like this one. What materials have been used in this way?

Go back now to your own planned building. What is its scale? Use a model person to indicate scale. What underlying frame-work will you need to support the building? How thick will the beams have to be? What shape will they be? You could use straws or cardboard beams in your model.

Try to specify which building materials would be used in each part of your design. You may need to find out more about the properties of each. How strong is your design? How well would it stand up to the weight of the materials from which it was made, and the wind? Did you have to make changes from your original plan as you thought more about its construction?

...t and post system of building used in the ...world is still in use today. Stone and concrete ...ak in tension because they have faults in them ...cause cracks. This limits the distance between ...s.

The arch, domes and vault system of construction was used by the Romans. It became the basis of Byzantine, Romanesque and Gothic styles of architecture. What materials would they be built from?

What materials are used in similar structures today?

...his office building is glass faced. As ...lass cannot support the structure, it ...ust be hung like a curtain from the frame of the building. How well do you think this building fits in with its surroundings? Does it look friendly or unfriendly? What are buildings with glass walls like to work in?

With the development of reinforced concrete, a structure could be made all of one piece. The concrete is reinforced or made stronger with metal rods running through it. Such one-piece structures are called monolithic, from the Greek 'one stone'.

Somewhere to LIVE

Housing is a basic human necessity; we all need a roof over our heads.

There are many people with nowhere to live. They may be whole families, young people who have left home, or those who have lost their jobs and their homes. What happens to these people?

We can either own our own flat or house, or rent one. In groups, research the following questions and report back.

■ Who provides houses and flats for rent?
■ Who provides them for sale?
■ Why do some people prefer to rent rather than buy?
■ What are the advantages of buying?

■ Find out what percentage of homes in your area are privately owned, privately rented, rented from the local council or from elsewhere.
■ Do the houses in these different groups look different? Are they different sizes?

Which groups of people need special housing? Discuss this in groups and make a list.

This family lives in bed and breakfast accommodation.

Homes have been made in derelict warehouses, redundant churches and vacant British Rail waiting rooms. Can you think of any other unusual homes?

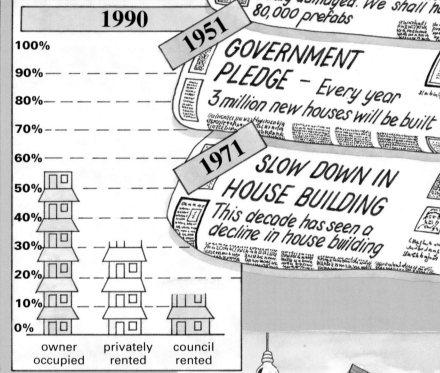

1915

100%
90%
80%
70%
60%
50%
40%
30%
20%
10%
0%

owner occupied   privately rented   council rented

1990

100%
90%
80%
70%
60%
50%
40%
30%
20%
10%
0%

owner occupied   privately rented   council rented

1920 HOMES FIT FOR HEROES
A massive house building programme is under way

1945 WARTIME DESTRUCTION
During the war 200,000 houses were destroyed and 3 million badly damaged. We shall have 80,000 prefabs

1951 GOVERNMENT PLEDGE – Every year 3 million new houses will be built

1971 SLOW DOWN IN HOUSE BUILDING
This decade has seen a decline in house building

What kind of house do you live in? Is it on a modern estate, in a high rise block of flats or in a terrace of older housing? Find out when your home was built. Are the other houses in your street of the same age?

Find out about the pattern of housing in your town. How many were built before World War I? How many are newly built? How many are inter-war housing, that is, built between the two world wars? How many are postwar, built after World War II?

What kind of people do you think live in a squat? What pressures may have forced them to live this way?

You have no permission or legal right to be here.

But the house was empty. One in 25 houses and flats in the country are empty.

HOUSING *layout*

THE SOONEST REACHED AT ANY TIME

GOLDERS GREEN
(HENDON AND FINCHLEY)

The basic ingredients in designing housing layouts are the houses and spaces.

In very early settlements, houses were mixed in with other buildings. In the 18th century, city housing was built as continuous terraces: often curved to form a crescent or circus (complete circle) or a square, with gardens in the middle. Some of our most elegant streets were built at this time. Then in the 19th century with industrial expansion many people began to move to the towns which grew rapidly. Rows of terraced houses were built close to factories. Why was this?

Those who could afford it moved out to the suburbs. The Garden City movement grew.

Find out more about Garden Cities and New Towns. When and where were they built? How big were they?

After World War I more houses were built around the edge of towns and this continued after World War II. At the same time some of the earlier terraced houses were declared slums and were cleared and new estates built in the inner cities.

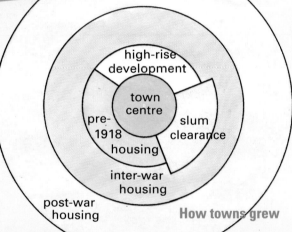

high-rise development

town centre

pre-1918 housing

slum clearance

inter-war housing

post-war housing

How towns grew

Imagine you lived on the Garden City estate below. What are the advantages and disadvantages? Think about moving around by car or on foot. Think about the size and shape of gardens, the land at the back. Try using a Townscape Notation analysis from page 7. Count the number of houses. How many households do you think live in this area? How does this compare with the number living in the rows of terraced houses illustrated?

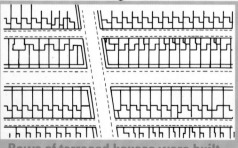

Rows of terraced houses were built in the 19th century next to factories.

This is an example of the Garden City type of layout. It is still popular today with many estate builders.

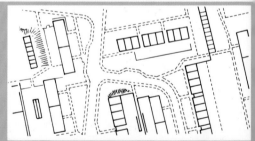

This type of layout is called Radburn layout. Compare it with the other layouts on this page. What are the differences?

In the 1960s housing estates of high-rise blocks of flats were built by councils on land which had been cleared of slum terraced housing.

In groups discuss why you think these types of flats were popular with architects, planners and councils at that time. What are the advantages and disadvantages of this type of housing?

My House

My Garden

Our Court

Why is it important to define territories in housing areas? Different spaces create different feelings. Small groups of houses around a space create a feeling of safety, comfort and privacy. What feelings are created by large open spaces?

Design some housing layouts for yourself. Think about:

Avoiding boring landscape/townscape

- Vary the shape of houses
- Vary the size and scale of houses
- Vary the degree of enclosure – use trees, fences and walls
- Vary the levels
- Stagger blocks – don't put them in rows
- Let one space lead to another.

Roads

- Main roads
- Local roads
- Small access roads for groups of houses
- Cycle tracks.

The environment

- The microclimate
- Air movement – make windbreaks
- Daylight and sunlight.

It is important to consider where cars and bicycles can be parked. List all the different places they can be left in a housing estate. What are the advantages and disadvantages of each?

Designers have to think about transport to housing areas and within them. Think about all the ways people and goods travel about housing areas and between them. When designing a housing layout, it is also important to make sure all the houses receive enough daylight and sunlight. How can this be done?

Home sweet HOME

For most people their house is the most important place in their lives.

Our cities and towns contain many different types and styles of house. Why they were built in their various forms is not only a story about architecture. It is also about life in those times, about fashion, and the materials and technology available. Look at these examples and see if you can give reasons for the style.

From the appearance and architectural detail of a house you can often tell how old it is.

Medieval 1200–1700

High chimney
Slate or thatched roof
Leaded windows: small panes
Oak framed: panels filled with wattle and daub, later bricks used in herringbone pattern

These were the first prefabricated buildings. The carpenter or builder would cut the wood to size and shape it in his yard, temporarily put it together and then transport it to the site to be built. Do you recognize this style of building? Can you name any towns or cities with buildings similar to this?

Regency 1800–1830

Stucco walls painted in pastel wash
Curving front walls
Porch
Curved fanlight
Large front door
Shallow bay windows

Regency style developed out of Georgian and had softer lines, but was also influenced by Oriental and Egyptian designs in the ironwork and porches. Many spa and coastal towns have Regency buildings. Do you know of any?

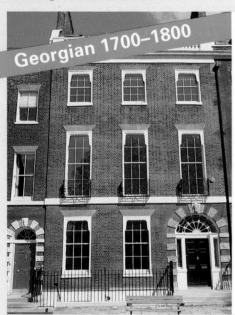

Georgian 1700–1800

Slate roof
Square windows act as a full stop
12 standard-size small panes per window
Brick walls
Slightly shorter windows
Wrought iron balconies
Main living room with tall windows for grandeur
Semi-circular fanlight
Large panelled front door
Short windows for solidarity

Georgian houses are elegant and can be recognized by their balance, symmetry and sense of proportion. This is true not only of the whole building but also of individual parts.
Discuss in groups what is meant by these words. Can you name a famous Georgian town?

Victorian 1830–1900

Slate roof
Brick built walls
Sash windows
Large window panes
Square fanlight
Bay window
Stone mullions
Tiled path to front door

The inventive Victorians improved production and building techniques. Bricks were mass produced, sheet glass was manufactured and transport was improved. Terrace after terrace of houses were built. Many still remain today.
Find examples of this style in your area, and make a sketch of them. Are there any variations on the design described above? Make a note of them.

High ornate chimney
Tile roof
Gables
Small window panes
Leaded windows
Red brick walls often tile hung

By 1890 architects began designing 'quaint and pretty' country cottages on the edge of towns, in 'garden suburbs'. They were looking back to an earlier age and were part of the Arts and Crafts Movement, which influenced designs of furniture and wallpaper.
Find out more about this movement.
Can you see similarities with another style?

After World War I many local councils copied the idea and built cottage estates, with houses for rent. They were plainer in appearance, with little decoration.

Semi-detached suburban 1920–present

Red tile roof
Tudor style cladding
Casement window
Square bay window
Stained glass window
Pebble dash infill between 'Tudor' cladding

Between the two world wars there was a tremendous demand for new houses to buy. Buyers wanted their houses to look different from council houses but not too outrageous. Today semi-detached houses are still very popular with builders, house buyers and building societies. Why do you think this is so?

System-built 1950–present

Cross wall reinforced concrete construction
Glass fibre panels
Aluminium window frames

During the 1950s and 1960s, new housing types were imported from France and Scandinavia. In this new 'system building', the building parts were prefabricated and put together on site by cranes. They were described as functionalist; that is, they looked like what they were and their appearance showed how they were made. Many of these housing estates are now being refurbished or demolished. Find out if there are any in your area.

Look at your area. Try to identify the different types and styles of houses. Take some photographs or make sketches and label them like those illustrated on this spread. Imagine you were designing a house. What style would you choose? Would you borrow design ideas from other countries? Carry out a survey of your friends and relatives to see which house type and style they prefer.

TODAY *and*

TOMORROW

Will the houses of tomorrow look very modern and new, or be imitations of past styles?

Many of the new houses being built today are in the style of Georgian or Tudor homes. Modern designs like the one in the photograph are often found only in large cities. Builders and developers think the general public dislike very modern styles. What do you think?

Think about the housing of the future. Make a list of the materials which will be available, and the technology you could use. Imagine how new materials and technology will change the appearance of buildings. Sketch your house of the future.

The appearance of our houses also comes from smaller architectural details. Look at these pictures and try to match them with the styles of houses on the previous spread.

Stained glass windows have been popular since Victorian times. Find examples of stained glass windows in your area. Look at the shapes, colour and patterns. Popular subjects are birds, flowers and sunrays. What subjects can you find?

People change the appearance of their houses to make them more personal to themselves and to suit their needs. Sometimes they change or add a different style or material. Think about the ways in which the appearance of a house can be changed. Find as many examples of such changes in your area as you can. Make sketches or take photographs.

Some people believe that when houses are altered, traditional materials and designs should be used to keep the same style. In groups, discuss whether you agree or disagree with this.

Make a collection of leaflets, or illustrations from home improvement magazines, of doors, windows, conservatories, door furniture etc. Your local DIY store or builders' merchant should be able to help. Try to identify the different styles and compare them with the original styles from the information on this and the previous spread. Imagine that you were making improvements to your house or flat. Which would you choose?

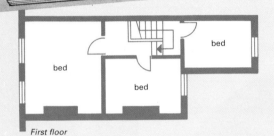

* Bedrooms on quiet side of house
* Living rooms light and airy with a view and sun in the morning
* Bedroom/study downstairs for elderly or disabled guests
* Downstairs cloakroom with shower
* Master bedroom with bathroom en suite and morning sun

Getting down to
DETAIL

These are some of the detailed requirements which a designer has to consider.

When architects design houses they need to think about the people who are to live in them.

They need to consider people's activities and the spaces needed, as well as how the house will look, how it will be built and the materials to be used.

A house can be described as a machine for living. The size of the rooms and spaces and the way in which they are arranged is important, if it is to work successfully.

As an architect, how do you choose the best room size to suit the purpose? What would you need to think about?

bed

bed

bed

First floor

kitchen

bath

living

dining

yard

alley

Ground floor

Lifestyles have changed over the years and these have lead to changes in the size and layout of houses. In groups, discuss some of the changes since the late 19th century. Ask your grandparents or older people that you know what changes they have seen in the size and internal design of houses. Make a list of things that you think are essential for a comfortable and efficient house. Think about houses of the future. What new technology could affect their design?

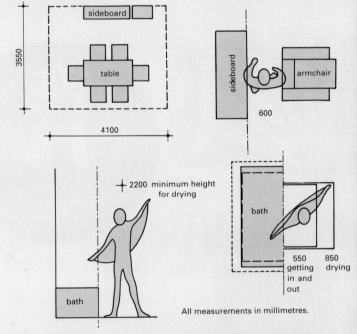

sideboard

3550

table

4100

sideboard

armchair

600

+ 2200 minimum height for drying

bath

bath

550 getting in and out

850 drying

All measurements in millimetres.

These suggestions have come from the Department of the Environment (DOE). The data came from various experts in furniture making, and other design specialists.

Carry out your own research. Take measurements of different types of furniture and equipment in your house and the amount of space needed to use them. Do not forget to measure height.

The interior of our houses should be like our clothes; warm, comfortable and practical. They should also say something about us; express our individual personalities. How can this be done? There are many different styles of furniture and decoration to choose from.

Country Style

Post-Modern

Just as important as the windows are the curtains or blinds. Why do we have curtains?

The way in which a room is lit is very important, for both the look of the room and the activities that are going on inside. Make a list of the different types of lighting you know. In groups, make recommendations for different rooms.

City Traditional

The first impression of a room comes from the colours, textures, furniture and lighting. Also of importance are the practical items, such as light switches and doorknobs. Can you think of more examples?

Keeping a house secure is also important. List the different ways this can be done. Think about which areas are the most easily broken into.

Walls provide the background for furniture and fabrics. What are the most common ways of decorating them? Are there any other ways?

High Tech

Look at these descriptions. Which fit the style in the photos?

- Romantic, nostalgic, comfortable, natural.
- Tough, no-nonsense, undecorated, with minimal colours, sharp angles.
- Sophisticated, classical, nostalgic.
- Gentle, classical detail, with sharp lines, vivid colours, sharp patterns.

Think of the different rooms in your house and what you do in them. What impression do you want each room to give? Could they be busy, bright, welcoming, peaceful, quiet?

Think about the furniture you would put in each room. Decide on the style you would choose, the colours, patterns and textures. Collect pictures from magazines of different styles of decoration and furnishing.

Floors take a lot of wear from people walking, as well as taking the weight of furniture. They have to be practical as well as decorative. List some types of floor. What are the advantages and disadvantages of each, and in which room could you put them?

Building a HOUSE

Let's look at some of the techniques used to build a house.

How are roof structures made strong? What is the pitch of a roof?

Why are the walls two bricks thick with a hollow space between?

What are the advantages of a modern 'ring main' circuit?

What does brick bonding mean? Why is it important? Find out about the different patterns created.

What is a damp-proof course? What material is used?

Which rooms must have a water supply?

Why are the foundations necessary?

Roofing

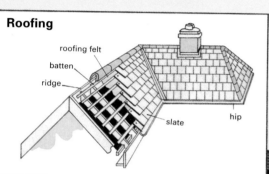

roofing felt
batten
ridge
slate
hip

Central heating system

water
cylinder
radiators
pump
boiler

Electric circuit

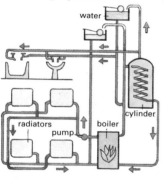

BUILDING A HOUSE - PLAN OF ACTION

CLIENT briefs

ENGINEER advises
Civil/Structural/
Mechanical/
Electrical

ARCHITECT
produces

QUANTITY SURVEYOR
Gives:
Costings/Prices

Sketch Plans

Working Drawings/
Costings

PLANNER
provides:
Planning
Permission/

BUILDING SURVEYOR
gives Building
Regulations
Approval/Inspects
Work

Tender/Contract

oversees
Building Works

BUILDER

lays Foundations

lays Drains

builds Walls to
Damp Proof Course

Wall and Windows

Roof

First Fix:
Carpentry
Plumbing
Electricals

Plaster Out:
Walls/Ceilings

Second Fix:
Plumbing
Electricals
Carpentry

Decoration/
Internal Tiling

COMPLETION

HAND OVER TO CLIENT

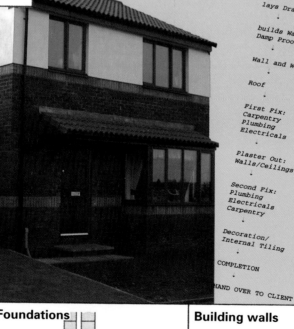

Damp proof course

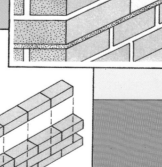

Foundations

Building walls

Energy conscious design

HEAT LOSS

Roof **10%**
Chimneys **20%**
Hot water wasted **10%**
Walls **20%**
Draughts **15%**
Floor **5%**

How can we stop losing heat and so reduce the amount of fuel needed?

* Space Heating **45%**
* Water Heating **16%**
* Cooking **8%**
* Lights and Appliances **31%**

How to help:
* Reduce energy demand
* Use renewable energy sources
* Use efficient appliances

What is meant by renewable energy? Where does it come from?

Wind turbine

Tidal barrier
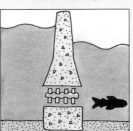

Solar tower
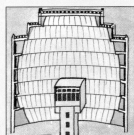

Hydroelectricity

Geothermal power
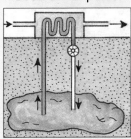

These two houses are built with passive collectors of solar heat.

Half of all energy used is used in buildings. Up to 14 per cent of the heat in our homes comes from the sun through windows and walls. In groups discuss how the architect, in designing houses, can improve upon this and make the best use of solar energy.

There are two solutions used in houses. Solar power is collected either through 'passive collectors' or 'active collectors' which often look like black-painted radiators on south facing roofs of houses. Have you seen any in your area? Find out how they work. Examples of 'passive collectors' of solar heat are windows, sloping glass roofs and conservatories.

WITCH OFF

SAVE IT

Make savings by using efficient appliances and cut back on use.

About a fifth of all energy used in houses goes to work cookers, lights and household appliances. Find out which uses the most energy. Make a list of things that can be done to cut back our use of energy. Imagine you were starting a campaign to save energy in houses. Write a plan of action.

Early shops displayed
signs to show what
goods were on sale.

SPEND SPEND SPEND

Buying and selling is an important part of our lives.

Have you ever thought what it would be like if there were no shops? Where would you buy the things you need and want?

Most of what we buy falls into one of two categories:

- Convenience goods; these are essentials, everyday shopping.
- Comparison goods; these are large purchases, where you usually compare prices before buying.

In the early Middle Ages there were no permanent shops or shopping centres. People bought and sold goods at open air markets, that is, from stalls placed outdoors in open areas in towns and villages. Later, individual shops appeared and gradually became recognizable as the kind we see in towns today.

It is permitted that a market be held every Wednesday between the hours of 6 in the morn and noon, for the sale of fresh produce and other goods. It will be held in the town square to the north of the Town Hall and by the Market Cross, the symbol of fair trading. No manner of person may buy or sell but with true weights and measures.

Think about the last time you visited a market. In groups, discuss your memories of the place. Include:

- The type of goods sold
- The way in which they were displayed
- The noises you heard
- The colours and patterns you saw
- The smells you liked and disliked.

What would it be like to be a stall holder, a shopper or the owner of a shop near the market? Can you think of any problems or conflicts that might arise?

Keep a diary of everything you and your parents buy in one week, and where the items came from. Did you shop around to compare prices and quality? Why did you choose to go to those particular shops? Was it the wide choice of goods, the attractiveness of the display, or how convenient it was to visit the shop, or some other reason?

The first shops were the front rooms of houses where craftsmen sold what they had made. There were no shop fronts. The goods were hung up in the window and large signs hung outside the house.

By the 19th century, market halls became important features in our towns. Some of them specialized in certain types of goods.

As trade developed, selling became as important as making. Shops, still the ground floors of houses, became places where anything was sold. Think about the advantages and disadvantages of being a shopkeeper in those times.

With better roads and railways people were able to move around towns and districts and compare the prices and the quality of goods. Shopkeepers had to compete for trade. Shop fronts were put in which reflected the fashion, materials and technology of their day. How the shop fronts looked are very important and have changed the way our towns look.

**Covent Garden
Flower Hall**

Make a study of shop fronts in your area. Make notes on:

- The materials used
- The decoration
- The colours
- The lettering.

Describe the overall effect they have. They may be, for example, amusing, welcoming, or boring.

Victorians used cast iron or tiles and shop fronts became heavy and ornate.

Make lists of convenience goods and comparison goods. Add to each item which type of shop you would find them in. Also add in which part of a town or city you would find such shops.

With the discovery of new materials such as Formica, modern shop fronts became flat and stark.

The CHOICE is yours

With Victorian times came the new age of shopping and shopkeeping.

Fashionable, freely accessible, walk-around bazaars and arcades were built in major cities. Marks and Spencer started off as a Penny Bazaar. Have your ever visited a Victorian Arcade? What was it like?

Why do you think that bazaars and arcades were fashionable? What modern inventions and discoveries helped in their development? Think about how they were built, the materials used, and the lighting.

" The Central Arcade is Edwardian Elegance in glass, decorated faience (glazed pottery) and terazzo.'

Compare the shopping arcade with the 'out of town' shopping centres on pages 28–29. List the similarities and differences. Think about colour, materials, patterns, shapes and construction.

Look at the floor pattern in the Newcastle arcade. Find out about terazzo tiling. When was it first used? Where and how are the tiles made? Try designing some floor patterns for yourself.

Look at the arcade's decoration. What other colours, decorative patterns and themes would have been used in these times?

SELFRIDGE'S
Dedicated to Woman's Service
Needs – the Man's Best Buyin
Stocks at London's Lowest P
NOW OPEN TO THE WO

"London receiving her
Newest Institution"

HMV
KNOW HMV · KNOW MUSIC

C&A

BhS

RKS & SPENCER

John Menzies

WH SMITH

By the middle of the last century multiple shops and chain stores started to appear throughout the country. The first were WH Smith and John Menzies. Make a list of the chain stores and multiples in your area. What type of buildings do they occupy? How can you recognize them as part of a chain? What is meant by 'house style'?

Co-operative Societies were amongst the first large scale retailers. The idea was based on 'honest dealing', that is, on co-operation rather than competition. Find out more about the co-operative movement. Do you have a Co-op store in your town? Where did Co-ops originate? What is meant by the 'dividend'? Did all these shops look alike?

In the history of shopping, the department store is only a recent development. Most started as a grocer's or draper's store. Choose a department store near you and in groups find out as much as you can about it. When was it opened? In which part of town was it located? Was it built as a store? What did it sell? Has it extended? How was it laid out inside? How many floors were there? Was there a lift or escalators? How were goods paid for?

Gordon Selfridge opened his first department store in London, and advertised it as providing all the facilities needed for a day out on a shopping trip. What facilities would he have had to provide? What are the major attractions of a department store? Are department stores still as attractive today? What changes have been made?

Which of the following were responsible for the growth of multiple and chain stores ?	A lot	some	not much
Local demand			
Bulk buying			
Greater prosperity			
Rapid Distribution			
Variety of goods -wide choice			
Concentration on single product			
Greater advertising			
Better design of shops			

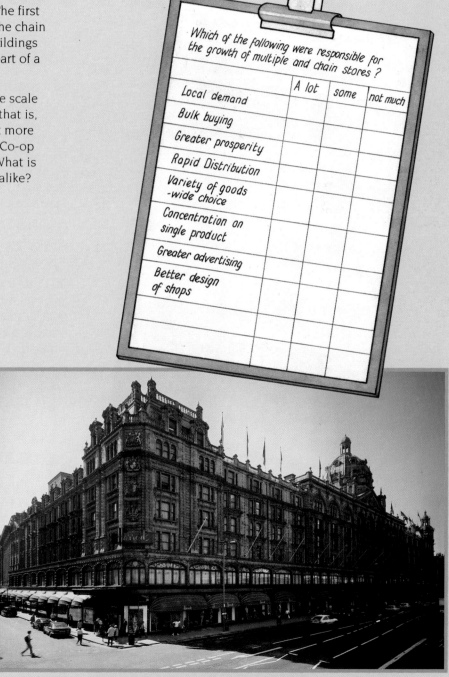

Department stores were impressive buildings in town and city centres. They often took up whole blocks, with roads around two sides, at least two entrances and exits, and large display windows.

Coventry precinct

(Map labels: department store, Corporation Street, gardens, variety store, Market Way, The Precinct, Smithford Way, variety store, variety store, variety store, multi-storey car park, upper level walk and shops, multi-storey car park, Hertford Street, buses only, hotel, bank, Post Office, Cross Cheaping)

Planned SHOPPING

After World War II, grand new shopping centres were built to replace the bomb-damaged town centres.

New towns were also created with new planned shopping centres within them.

In the 1960s fully enclosed shopping centres were built. Why do you think this was so?

How do you think the design of shops has changed since then? Why are supermarkets more popular than small grocers? Think about corner shops. They are often open all hours. Compare them with supermarkets or superstores. Are they more convenient? Imagine you are elderly, work late or do not own a car. Where would you shop?

The ethnic origin of small shop owners has changed. Traders of Greek, Italian, West Indian, Pakistani and Indian origin now own many small shops.

Eldon Square in Newcastle is said to be 'knitted into the fabric of the city'.

RICHARDS

Which factors do you think help to make a good shopping centre?

✓ or ✗

1. Pedestrians can move about freely and safely
2. Attractive, efficient and comfortable
3. Building materials & construction can withstand vandalism
4. Variety of shops
5. Attractive shop front designs
6. Good road access for cars and buses
7. Adequate car parking and bus stops
8. Department stores, chain stores, multiples
9. Supermarkets
10. Places to sit

Visit a shopping centre near you. Make a note of the different types of shop. Which shop do you think attracts the most shoppers? Where is it located? Does it encourage shoppers to walk along the street, across a square, past other shops?

26

Of course 40 years ago, there was no such thing as self service. We had personal service.

Who do you think mainly decides on the design of a superstore? Why do you think most superstores look alike?

Retailer

Architect

'Footprints'

r layout for our erstore should show:

* circulation space
* sales area
* warehouse / storage area
* shelf units
* preparation areas
* staff facilities

The first DIY sheds were built in the suburbs of many towns. Why do you think this was so? Now they are being built in 'retail parks'. Find out more about these sheds. How big are they? How are they constructed? What materials are used? How are they being decorated?

These large nondescript buildings could be warehouses, factories or offices. The outside appearance does not indicate what happens inside. The interior can be a series of 'stage sets' for different activities. The interior designer is very important in designing shops.

These shops were in the Killingworth Centre in North Tyneside, and have been demolished.

❝One of the most notable features of urban life in the last 30 years has been the new style shopping facilities – pedestrianized streets, shopping precincts, hypermarkets, superstores, out of town shopping centres.❞

SHOPPING
for pleasure

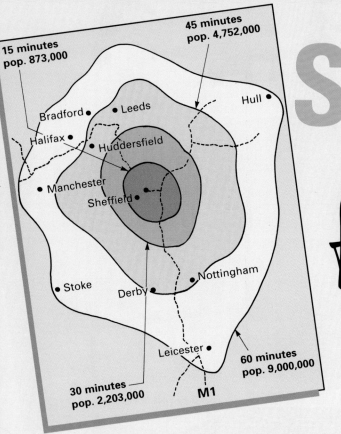

15 minutes pop. 873,000

45 minutes pop. 4,752,000

Bradford • • Leeds

Hull •

Halifax • • Huddersfield

• Manchester

Sheffield •

• Stoke

Derby •

• Nottingham

Leicester •

30 minutes pop. 2,203,000

M1

60 minutes pop. 9,000,000

Out of town shopping centres are part of the latest trend in shopping for pleasure.

It is said that town and city centres are becoming less important because of the growth in travel and electronic communications. The Meadowhall Centre in Sheffield was built outside the city centre. Its site was a 138-acre redundant steelworks. It claims to be the most accessible centre in Britain, with nine million people living less than an hour's journey away.

What do you think you have to provide in a new shopping centre to attract visitors from a long distance? Make a list. Think about:

- Car parking spaces
- Different kinds of shops
- Other facilities.

Café Rome

TO THE ROMAN FORUM

A town is built up over time. It has variety and a history. Out of town shopping centres have no history, so they try to provide this instantly by giving certain areas 'themes'. Imagine you were planning an out of town shopping centre. What themes would you choose? Think about the different materials, colours,

lighting, seating, signposting and graphics you would choose for each of your theme areas.

'Spend, spend, spend. The eighties became known as the decade we went shopping – it is still one of the most popular leisure activities.'

METRO CENTRE

A unique shopping and leisure experience. Europe's largest out of town shopping centre with 3 miles of spacious, tree-lined shopping malls, is a shoppers' paradise. The 10-screen cinema offers the ultimate in entertainment. The GX Superbowl 28-lane bowling centre has brought together today's technology and luxury. The Metrocentre offers more than 50 places to eat and drink, including traditional pubs, gourmet meals, quick snacks. Metroland is a fantasy land of fairground rides and attractions. A magical kingdom landscaped with water-falls, streams and clouds.

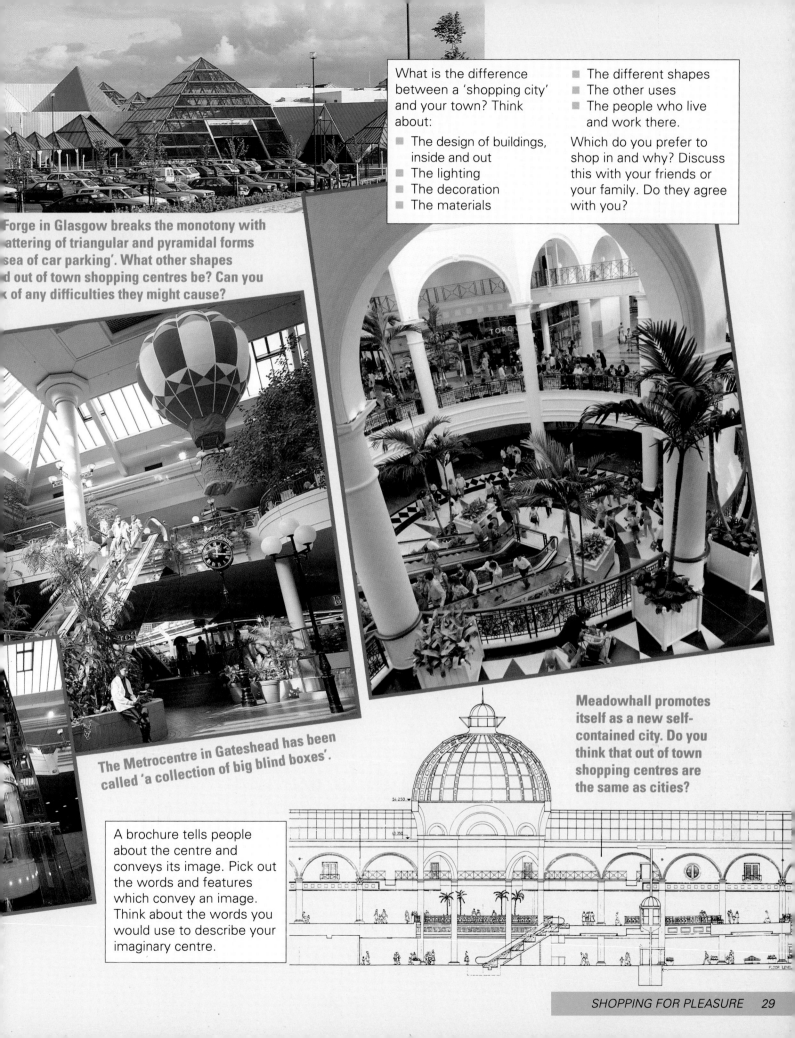

What is the difference between a 'shopping city' and your town? Think about:

- The design of buildings, inside and out
- The lighting
- The decoration
- The materials
- The different shapes
- The other uses
- The people who live and work there.

Which do you prefer to shop in and why? Discuss this with your friends or your family. Do they agree with you?

Forge in Glasgow breaks the monotony with attering of triangular and pyramidal forms sea of car parking'. What other shapes d out of town shopping centres be? Can you k of any difficulties they might cause?

The Metrocentre in Gateshead has been called 'a collection of big blind boxes'.

Meadowhall promotes itself as a new self-contained city. Do you think that out of town shopping centres are the same as cities?

A brochure tells people about the centre and conveys its image. Pick out the words and features which convey an image. Think about the words you would use to describe your imaginary centre.

FUN *and* GAMES

Leisure time is an important part of our everyday life.

The Water Place is located in the centre of Bolton. What advantages and disadvantages might such a location have? Discuss the ways in which leisure can play a part in bringing a town centre back to life.

There is a new concept in ice skating – Leisure Ice! At the Dome in Doncaster, 'liquid water has a sister – frozen water'. You can both swim and skate under one roof.

In the past, working people had no leisure time, except, if they were lucky, an annual summer holiday.

Nowadays, leisure is big business! Leisure sites may be:

- National sites, visited mainly by large numbers of people once or twice a year. Examples are theme parks, holiday villages and heritage attractions.
- Local sites, visited by smaller numbers of people on a more regular basis. Examples are cinemas, sports centres, pubs and restaurants.

We can now see 'leisure buildings' in our cities. People have more leisure time, because the working week has become shorter. People retire earlier. This, together with the fitness and health boom has led to the growth in 'leisure architecture'.

The 1960s sports centres were described as having an image of competitive, sporting excellence.

By the 1980s sports centres became known as leisure centres. The image is one of relaxed leisure. Do you have any ideas about what might have caused this change in image? If you were to design a leisure centre, which of these images would you design for? Is it possible to design for both? How?

...wer Park in Poole, Dorset has a ten-screen ...nema with nightclub, a Megabowl, a water ...rk and an ice rink, plus a mixture of small ...ops, restaurants and office space.

...Do the tower, and the red ...nd white structure in the ...hotograph remind you of ...ny other places of ...ntertainment? What sort ...f image does the complex ...onvey?

...he scale of leisure ...uildings is very large. Do ...ou see anything in the ...esign of this building ...hich attempts to break ...he scale down?

...he roof of a leisure centre ...as to span a large area ...ecause of the activities ...hat go on underneath. ...Why is height, as well as ...idth, important?

Look at this photograph of a model of Doncaster Leisure Complex. List as many different areas of activity as you can. Many of the activity areas seem to 'flow' one into another. How do you think this effect is achieved?

Are any areas very distinct or separate? If so, why?

How do you think changes in level affect the movement of people about the building? Which ones add to the excitement of an activity?

Note down the ways in which using this model would help you to understand the building better than a photograph would.

I'm bored. What can I do today?

...hat do you do when you ...e bored? Where do you ...? Are any of the places ...u go to in your leisure ...ne like the ones shown ...re? Ask your friends ...hich of these activities ...ey would choose. What ...out your parents and ...andparents? Would their ...oices be the same or ...fferent?

Many leisure centres are sited out of town, and have to serve several small villages and towns.

Design a multi-coloured leaflet to be used as part of a marketing drive to increase the number of visitors. Collect brochures and leaflets from leisure centres in your area to help you.

Think about:
- The information to be included
- Where it would be distributed
- How it will attract attention
- What size it would be.

What other things might you do in order to market a centre?

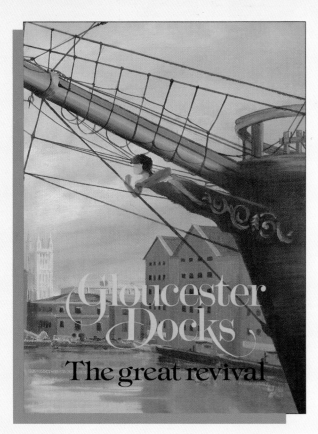

OUT and ABOUT

Some people like to visit towns and cities which are full of history and where historical buildings are part of the townscape. Is there a trail for your town, city or village? You could devise a trail for your area, with some friends. They could also help test it out.

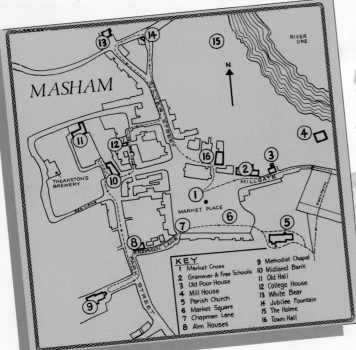

MASHAM

RIVER URE

KEY
1 Market Cross
2 Grammar & Free Schools
3 Old Poor House
4 Mill House
5 Parish Church
6 Market Square
7 Chapman Lane
8 Alm Houses
9 Methodist Chapel
10 Midland Bank
11 Old Hall
12 College House
13 White Bear
14 Jubilee Fountain
15 The Holme
16 Town Hall

Town trails are popular ways of exploring a place.

In Centre Parcs, Nottingham, buildings and spaces have been created just for leisure activities.

Tourist Information ℹ

Where would you put a Tourist Information Point in your town?

What sort of information could be displayed? Sketch a design for a TIP. Think about:

■ Size   ■ Materials
■ Shape   ■ Colour
■ The weather.

The English Tourist Board want tourists to be able to obtain information even when Tourist Information Centres are shut. This is done through a Tourist Information Point (TIP), a display panel prominently placed.

...lidays and day trips are ...special use of leisure time. ...ourism is big business.

Which of the places shown on this spread would you visit and which activities would you choose? Would your friends and relations pick the same as you?

...uring the last century, holidays at health resorts, or ...pa towns as they were known, were popular. These ...were the forerunners of the Victorian seaside resorts with their piers, like this one in Brighton.

STEP BACK IN TIME
— AND LIVE THE LIFE OF 1900 —

Wigan Pier was where the colliery railway met the Leeds-Liverpool Canal

WIGAN PIER

Where History Come...

The warehouses built at Wigan are now used to interpret Victorian seaside holidays. Do you think that this is an appropriate use?

Interpretation Centres have become an important part of tourism. These centres tell (interpret) stories about a place in an interesting way.

The story told at an Interpretation Centre might be about the area's history, or its wildlife, or anything that visitors or residents might find interesting and entertaining.

In groups compare the pictures of Centre Parcs and the Victorian resort of Brighton. Are there any similarities between the activities and entertainments on offer?

What similarities and differences can you see between the two environments? Look particularly at:
- Shape
- Materials
- Patterns, and
- Structures.

Imagine that it has been suggested that a Visitor Centre be developed in your area. Decide on the theme or story to be interpreted. Choose an existing building which might be suitable for this use. Put forward some suggestions as to what should be included in a brief for the design of the centre.

Room to breathe

'Pocket parks' have been created recently on derelict sites. They provide small oases of greenery and open space amid the hard buildings and surfaces of cities. Why do you think they are called 'pocket parks'?

People living and working in urban areas need open spaces such as parks.

Parks of different sizes and designs in our towns and cities are important to us. They also affect the way our built environment looks.

Imagine you are a landscape architect and you are designing a pocket park.

- Where in your neighbourhood might be an appropriate site?
- Who would the park be for?
- What might the users want in it?

Write down a list.

Think about plants, materials, patterns and colours.

Sketch a design for some railings for your park. Who is going to look after the park and maintain it?

Nature parks have appeared in cities over the last ten years or so. They have been created by schools and communities wishing to study the natural environment on their doorstep. Can you think of any other benefits nature parks may give?

Butterflies / Habitats

Species	Caterpillar Plants	Nectar Plants
Small White	Cabbage, cauliflower, rape, garlic mustard, nasturtium, mignonette, Arabis Aubretia.	Arabis, Aubretia
Large White	Cress nasturtium mignonette.	Arabis Aubretia
Orange Tip	Garlic mustard, dames' violet, lady's smock, sweet rocket, honesty	Bugle, forget-me-not and yellow wallflowers
Meadow Brown	Grasses, especially Poa species eg. Poa annua (common meadow grass)	Hayfield flora, Buddleia, thistles, Umbellifers
Speckled Wood	Grasses, especially couch grasses	Bramble, Buddleia

A landscape architect thinks about building walls and paths as well as about plants. Look at this specification for laying concrete blocks as a surface for pedestrians and vehicles. If you were going to use this material in your park what would be the specifications necessary?

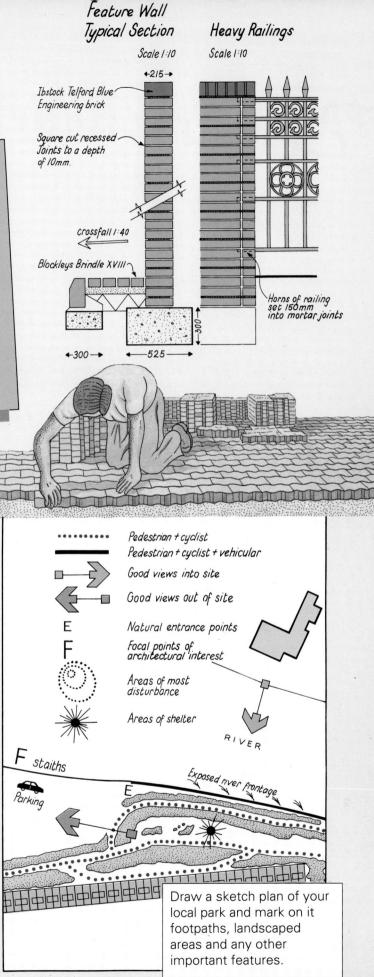

Feature Wall Typical Section
Scale 1:10

- Ibstock Telford Blue Engineering brick
- Square cut recessed Joints to a depth of 10mm.
- crossfall 1:40
- Blockleys Brindle XVIII

←215→

←300→ ←525→ 500

Heavy Railings
Scale 1:10

- Horns of railing set 150mm into mortar joints

...ty	Natural Ground Beneath Road	Thickness of Sub-base	Sub-base Material Fully Compacted	Surface
...nt use by ...ercial vehicles	Gravels, Rock etc. Sand Sandy Clay Silty Clay Heavy Clay	80 mm 150 mm 200 mm 300 mm 500 mm	Granular material crushed rock, hardcore or old concrete	Blocks laid on 50 mm coarse sand, then vibrated to full compaction.
...sional use by ...nercial vehicles	Gravels, Rock etc. Sand Sandy Clay Silty Clay Heavy Clay	80 mm 150 mm 150 mm 250 mm 400 mm	Granular material crushed rock, hardcore or old concrete	Blocks laid on 50 mm coarse sand, then vibrated to full compaction.
...sional use by ...commercial ...cles	Gravels, Rock etc. Sand. Sandy Clay Silty Clay Heavy Clay	No sub-base necessary 100 mm 200 mm 300 mm	Granular material crushed rock, hardcore or old concrete	Blocks laid on 50 mm coarse sand, then vibrated to full compaction.
...ate drives, ...estrian ...ways	Gravels, Rock etc. Sand Sandy Clay Silty Clay Heavy Clay	No sub-base necessary 100 mm 200 mm 300 mm	Granular material crushed rock, hardcore or old concrete	Blocks laid on 50 mm coarse sand, then vibrated to full compaction.
...vate paths	—	No sub-base necessary		Blocks laid on 50 mm coarse sand, then vibrated to a smooth surface.

Landscape architects design new landscapes and try to improve the appearance and use of existing areas. This drawing shows a 'landscape appraisal' of a site. What elements of the existing landscape has the landscape architect looked at and noted down on her plan?

Do you think these things might be important? Think about how they might be used in the new design for the site.

.... Pedestrian + cyclist
———— Pedestrian + cyclist + vehicular
→ Good views into site
← Good views out of site
E Natural entrance points
F Focal points of architectural interest
Areas of most disturbance
Areas of shelter

RIVER

F staiths
Parking
Exposed river frontage
E

Victorian town and city parks were often created on land owned by wealthy industrialists who wished to benefit the local population by creating 'peoples' gardens'. These parks were often named after the original owner. Are there any parks like these in your town or city? If so, what are they called? See what you can find out about their history.

Draw a sketch plan of your local park and mark on it footpaths, landscaped areas and any other important features.

Entertaining places

We all need to relax and enjoy ourselves.

We entertain ourselves in different ways: a show, a meal, a film or a chat with friends. Whatever we choose to do, there is a great variety of places and spaces to do it in.

At the beginning of this century, cafes, fairgrounds, shops, music halls and even railway arches were used for film shows. Early cinemas were built on the plan of traditional theatres and music halls: plain halls with their fronts (facades) covered in fairground-inspired decoration. They were known as 'electric palaces'. What uses do they now have?

1909 CINEMATOGRAPHIC ACT

Projection of films to take place in a fire resistant box separated from the auditorium

There are now many regulations about fire hazards in public buildings such as cinemas.

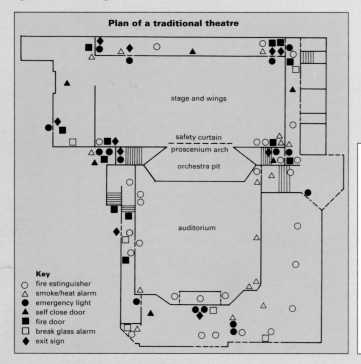

Plan of a traditional theatre

stage and wings

safety curtain
proscenium arch
orchestra pit

auditorium

Key
- ○ fire estinguisher
- △ smoke/heat alarm
- ● emergency light
- ▲ self close door
- ■ fire door
- □ break glass alarm
- ◆ exit sign

The electric palaces were dangerous places. There were frequent fires, because of the material films were made of.

Because of television, cinema audiences began to decline in the 1950s. To cater for smaller audiences and give more choice, many cinemas began to divide their internal space to make two or three screens instead of one.

Think about fire danger in relation to the following:
- Routes
- Stairs
- Distances between seats and exits
- Lighting
- Materials
- Signing
- Alarms
- Ventilation
- Firefighting equipment.

Think about advantages and disadvantages in altering cinemas in this way. Think about:
- Atmosphere
- Interior decorations
- Noise and acoustics
- Fire regulations.

Going to the pictures in the 1920s and 1930s was an event, an escape from the harsh realities of unemployment and poverty. Many of the interiors of the cinemas had fantasy character atmospheres. How do you think this was created?

Some of the cinemas were often considered to be 'blots on the townscape'. Do you think the scale, form and materials of this 1930 Odeon would be sympathetic to the High Street in which it was built?

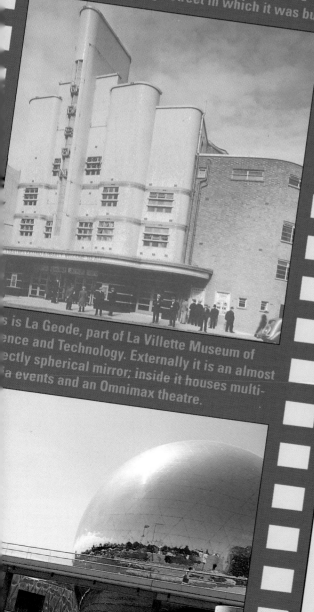

...is La Geode, part of La Villette Museum of ...ence and Technology. Externally it is an almost ...ectly spherical mirror; inside it houses multi- ...a events and an Omnimax theatre.

What do you think makes the Multiplex a new 'cinema experience' compared to the cinemas of the 1920s and 1930s? Think about:

- Technology
- Materials
- Style and fashion
- Acoustics.

Films are art and entertainment, but they are also technology. In the 1950s improvements in projection techniques led to wider screens. This was called 'Cinamascope'. To make room for it, some cinemas knocked down the proscenium arch. 'Cinerama' came later, with curved screens, but not many 'Cineramas' were created in Britain. Why do you think this was so?

'Omnimax' screens 'wrap around the audience'. Why are these cinema interiors not highly decorated like those of the 1930s? How can the technology of the Omnimax cinema determine the shape of a building?

In the Middle Ages, drama was an important part of urban life. Plays, usually religious ones, were performed in any available open space, usually in the market square or beside the cathedral. What sort of entertainment can we see in the streets of our towns and cities today?

At your LEISURE

NATIONAL THEATRE

How does the built environment show our changing leisure activities?

Prince Charles:
'The National Theatre is a clever way of building a nuclear power station in the middle of London without anyone objecting.'

Sir Denys Lasdun:
'The building retreats from the ground to allow for stunning views of London.'

Passer-by:
'But it's ugly. It looks like a cheese sandwich. And how do you get into it?'

What do you think Prince Charles meant? Do you agree with him? Do you think you should always be able to recognize a building from its external appearance? Sir Denys Lasdun is the architect who designed the building. Do you agree with his view of the design? What do you think was the most important issue for the passer-by?

One of the most important aspects in the design of theatres and music halls is the sound quality or acoustics. Why is this?

A popular way to relax and enjoy yourself is to eat out with friends. This might be at an American-style fast food outlet or at an expensive restaurant. Wherever is chosen, the atmosphere of the place is an important part of the enjoyment.

The Blue Elephant is a Thai restaurant in London. The design is based on a traditional Thai village.

List the different parts of the village which have been used in the interior design of the Blue Elephant. Imagine you were to create a restaurant interior based on a village near you. What parts of the village would you include in the design?

Little China on the Tyne

中國城

In English that's Chinatown

East meets West in Stowell Street, the heart of Newcastle's Chinese community and a gastronomique haven for stir-fry loving Geordies. Yet this bustling street which is now home to one of Britain's largest Chinese Communities, was once a small dark back lane.

Today you'll not only find the famous cluster of Chinese restaurants, but also a Chinese supermarket, community centre, and travel agent. A valuable pair of carved stone lions have been shipped from the Orient to stand guard over New-castle's Chinatown.

In some cities, Chinese restaurants are close together and have formed a 'Chinatown' within the city. In Newcastle, Manchester and London, Chinatowns are popular tourist attractions, as well as popular places for local residents. Have you visited any Chinatowns? What Chinese-style things do you find there?

Think about:

- Colours
- Decoration
- Signs
- Smells.

What other kinds of restaurant with foreign cuisine do you know? How do you recognize them?

What do you think of this street furniture and landscaping?

Find out about China's (or another country's) art: its symbols, sculpture and colours. Then sketch some ideas for seats, litter bins, plant containers for an area in that style.

From DARKNESS to LIGHT

Where we work, what we produce and how we produce it has an effect on us and on the environment.

Some people no longer have to work in purpose-built buildings. Some work from home, or even from cars. What major development in technology has allowed this to happen? Do you think it has given us more freedom, or other benefits?

In Britain in the middle of the 18th century everyone lived in villages, which were self sufficient. Most people worked on the land, with some in cottage industries such as weaving. By the middle of the 19th century, industry had moved into buildings called factories. Two inventions led to this move. One was the discovery of water power. What was the other?

Most of the early industries produced textiles. Early factories were not designed by architects but by their owners. They were brick buildings with timber floors. Fires were very common.

Imagine you were a mill owner whose mill had burnt down. What changes might you make in your next mill to prevent the same thing happening?

Think about:

■ Materials
■ Heating
■ Lighting
■ Construction.

Temple Mills in Leeds was styled on a 2000-year-old temple at Edfu in Egypt.

Manningham Mill in Bradford was designed in the style of an Italian walled hill town.

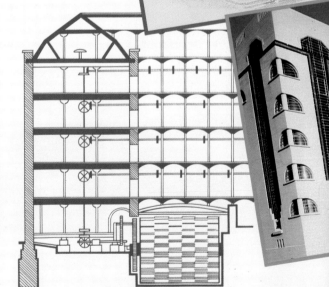

Early industrial buildings were designed around the transmission of power. How was the power transmitted in this building?
The top floor had no machinery and was used as a schoolroom on Sundays. Some of the mill workers were children.

Imagine you were a writer in 1838, when Temple Mills had just been built. Write a description of the building, using the following words once you have found out what they mean:

- Papyrus leaves
- Lotus flower capitals
- Winged solar discs
- Huge cornice.

Describe what you think might have been the reactions of the workers to this building.

Natural lighting was vital to the early mill buildings. Why was this? Why did it become even more important as machinery got bigger?

The Special Areas Act of 1937 created new industrial estates, called 'trading estates'. This was the first time that industrial areas had been planned and these estates were the forerunners of modern industrial estate layouts like the one above.

In Temple Mills 66 glass domes in the roof provided even illumination over the workroom floor.

Could this building be an office, a factory, a shop or a house?

The Manningham Mill buildings are 'listed', which means they are protected from demolition and alteration because of their architectural or historic importance. Find out if there are any listed buildings near you.

Manningham Mill is being converted into a hotel, offices, shops and a museum.

What advantages are there in having such a range of activities together? What do you think are the advantages of using old buildings in this way? To what use have any old industrial buildings in your area been put?

Modern microchip industries have developed rapidly over the last few years. Why are they called Sunrise industries?

What effect do you think microtechnology has had upon manufacturing industries and their buildings?

Between the two world wars many factories were built in dramatic styles, on prominent sites on main roads, set in lawns and floodlit at night. Why do you think this happened? Are there any factories like this near you?

THAMES VALLEY PARK
GROUND FLOOR PLAN

New industrial development now takes place alongside offices and other facilities in pleasant Business Parks or Science Parks. Do you have any Science or Business Parks near you? Describe them. Why are they located near to motorways and airports?

Canary Wharf in London is a North American-style office building with a central core of lifts and stairs and large floor areas.

OUT OF THE ARK

Many offices have sprung up in city and town centres.

This office block is on a difficult site on a traffic island next to the Hammersmith flyover in London. The architect is Ralph Erskine, who designed the housing in Byker (page 4). The office block has become known as Erskine's Ark.

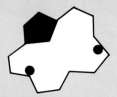

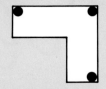

Burolandschaft Office (landscaped – German)
5 storeys

Traditional British Speculative Office
10 storeys

New British Speculative Office
10 storeys

Traditional North American Office
80 storeys

New North European Office
10 storeys

The dark areas are the 'cores': lifts and stairs form entrance points.

For each of the plans shown above, describe one advantage and one disadvantage of the layout. Choose one of the plans and sketch a building that could result from it.

Imagine that this is your first day at work in the Ark. Describe your thoughts on the way to work. What facilities do you expect there to be in this 'town under a roof'? Describe the environment that has been created and say whether you like it or not.

The interior of Erskine's Ark is a series of terraces and balconies, which are stepped down and are like small streets. Tenants in the building will be able to choose to have completely open or partitioned 'cellular' offices.

Some offices are built as the administrative headquarters of large international companies. In other cases developers build offices 'speculatively'. What do you think this means? In many cities, offices reflect international styles of design.

The Ark is a local landmark. The architect said that if the site had had more impressive surroundings, his design would have been more modest. Do you think he was correct in creating such an imposing building here? What do you feel about the scale and the form of the building in relation to the surroundings? Discuss these aspects in a group. Do you all agree?

Although the appearance of the outside of the building is important to Erskine, it is the ideas for the inside which really excited him. He hopes that the Ark will 'become a social environment ... a town under a roof'.

Putting the pieces together

We have looked at several different aspects of design. How does it work in practice?

Building and landscape design. This is the detailed design of buildings and spaces including materials, appearance and construction. Such designs are in three dimensions.

Urban design. This is concerned with the layout of roads and buildings, their efficiency and general arrangement. These designs are also in three dimensions.

Planning. This is concerned with la... general location of buildings and o... and with traffic circulation. These... in two dimensions.

The design of the built environment is made up of three elements, shown above.

The professionals involved in these three parts are architects, landscape architects, planners and engineers.

The built environment is where we live, work and play. How well the built environment works depends on how well it has been planned, designed and maintained, and how it is allowed to respond to meet present and future needs.

Imagine you are a town planner. What makes a good urban environment? Make a list of all the things you would provide in your town. Think about the basic needs of everyone and the special needs of some people. Think about the things which need to be next to each other and those which are better apart. Think about different kinds of transport between areas.

Town planning is concerned with land use. All developments, including new houses and new factories, require planning permission. Planners put together plans for an area; these may then be adopted and become official.

Find out about:
- Structure plans
- Unitary development plans
- Local plans
- Conservation areas
- Use classes order.

Town and city centres are different from the rest of a town or a city, but in what ways? What activities and buildings do you find there? How do you know you have arrived in the centre of a town or city? What effect do you think out of town shopping centres and business parks have on town centres?

A neighbourhood is an area in which we live and carry out other activities. Facilities other than housing are needed in neighbourhoods. What are they? Discuss your thoughts with a partner and pool your ideas.

Cities and towns have their problems. Planners, architects, landscape architects and engineers try to solve these problems.

Think of the problems that a city you know has. List the problems and beside them put down some possible solutions.

Different cities have different images. Are there any other descriptions which you would add to this list?

- Historical
- Industrial
- Market
- Spa or seaside
- Cultural.

Think of at least one town or city which fits each description.

A great deal of money and time is sometimes spent on changing the image of a city.

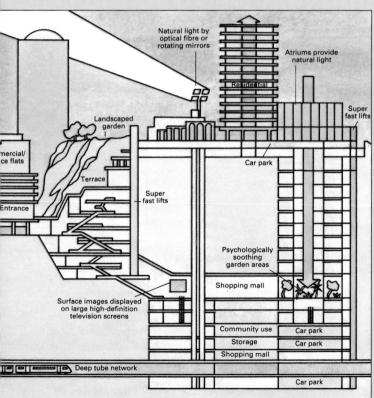

Natural light by optical fibre or rotating mirrors

Atriums provide natural light

Residential

Landscaped garden

Super fast lifts

mercial/ ce flats

Terrace

Car park

Entrance

Super fast lifts

Psychologically soothing garden areas

Shopping mall

Surface images displayed on large high-definition television screens

Community use | Car park
Storage | Car park
Shopping mall

Deep tube network

Car park

Two of the problems in urban areas are lack of space to expand and the high cost of land. One solution is the development of 'inner space': underground complexes of offices, shopping and leisure facilities. What do you think of this idea? Discuss it in groups.

What sort of built environment would you like to see in the future? Draw some plans and sketches to present your ideas.

Do you think we should all be involved in making decisions about the environment? You can become involved in many ways:

- Join a local environmental society
- Read the local papers so that you are aware of environmental issues
- Find out if there are any plans being put forward for the area in which you live
- Go along to any public meetings which are held, ask questions and voice your opinions.

Firstly and most importantly, *get to know your area*; its people, its places and its spaces; its potential, its problems and its needs. This book will give you some starting points for doing just that.

Acknowledgements

The authors would like to thank the following for their help and support: John Kean; Ailsa Kean; Lionel Hehir; Sam Hehir; Newcastle Architecture Workshop; numerous pupils and teachers in Newcastle upon Tyne and South Tyneside; the *Interactions* team; Michael Drage, Architect and Designer; Geoffrey Purves, Architect; Jane Darbyshire, Architect; and Eileen Adams, Educational Consultant.

The authors and publishers are grateful to the following for permission to reproduce photographs and real items:

Airpic, Aerial shot (p. 3); *Arcaid*, High Tech Interior/Richard Bryant (p. 19); *Architectural Association*, Parthenon, Athens/John Mosse (p. 9), St. Paul's Cathedral Interior/ A H Acland (p. 9), Schlumberger Research Centre, Cambridge/Valerie Bennett (p. 9), Sussex House converted from railway carriage/Luisa Auletta (p. 11), 18-Storey Point Blocks/Canon Parson (p. 13), Georgian House, Bedford Square, London/Valerie Bennett (p. 14), Victorian Terrace Houses, West Ham, London/John Bailey (p. 14), Doorway detail/Graham Shankland (p. 17), Porch detail/Pat Reed (p. 17), Half Timber Doorway/Hans Duttman (p. 17), Victorian Bay Stained Glass Windows/Andrew Higgott (p. 17), Electric Palace/Roger Whitehouse (p. 36), Canary Wharf/Tony Weller (p. 42), Oxford Street/John Linden (p. 45); *Australian Overseas Information Service, London*, Sydney Opera House (p. 8); *Barrie Smith*; La Geode (p. 37); *British Home Stores*, Logo (p. 25); *Bournville Village Trust*, Old English Style Cottage (p. 15); *Boys Syndication*; Country-Style Interior (p. 19); *Susan Bradley*, Toys 'R' Us Superstore (p. 27); *Permission of The British Library*, Covent Garden Flower Hall (p. 23); *British Nuclear Fuels plc*, Sellafield (p. 9); *Building Design Partnership*, Metroplex (p. 41), Thames Valley Park (p. 41); *Centre Parcs*, Interior of Centre Parcs, Nottingham (p. 32); *Chapman, Taylor and Partners*, Meadowhall Shopping Centre/Donald Innes (p. 29); *Cinema Theatre Association*, Exterior and Interior of 1930s Odeon (p. 37); *City Repro*, Central Arcade, Newcastle (p. 24), Eldon Square (p. 26), Eldon Garden (p. 26), Victorian Bandstand (p. 35); *C&A*, Logo (p. 25); *Communique*, Erskine's Ark (p. 42); Interior of Erskine's Ark (p. 43); © *Crown Copyright*, Maps (p. 12); *Denys Lasdun, Peter Softley Associates*, Milton Gate, London (p. 9); *Design Dimension*, Formica Shop Fronts (p. 23), Do It All/Roger Standen (p. 27); *Michael Drage Architects*, Completed House (p. 20); *Dubosc and Landowski Architects*, Givors, France (p. 21); *Edifice*, Wells Cathedral (p. 5), Brighton Pavilion (p. 8), Semi-detached Surburban House, Surrey (p. 15), Council Estate, Beacontree (p. 15), Tall Chimneys, Howe Green, Essex (p. 17), Sunburst Gate (p. 17), Stained Glass Galleon (p. 17), Regency Porch, Cheltenham (p. 17), Georgian Doorway, Bristol (p. 17), Holborn, Umbrellas (p. 23); *English Heritage Photographic Library*, Regency Buildings, Pelham Crescent (p. 14); Trellick Tower, London (p. 15); *Everyman Theatre, Cheltenham*, Theatre Plan (p. 36); *Faulkner Browns Architects*, The Water Place, Bolton (p. 30), Tower Park, Poole (p. 30), Model of Doncaster Leisure Complex (p. 31), Ice Rink, Doncaster (p. 30); *Geoffrey Purves Partnership*, Blue Elephant Restaurant, London (p. 39); *Gloucestershire Tourism*, Brochure of Gloucester Docks (p. 32); *Greater Glasgow Tourist Board*, Glasgow's Miles Better logo (p. 45); *Guildhall Library*, Burlington Arcade (p. 24); *Steve Harris Photography*, Trading Estate (p. 41); *Harrods Ltd*, External view of Harrods (p. 25); *Harrogate Resort Services*, Masham Town Trail (p. 32); *HMV*, Logo (p. 25); *ICCE Photolibrary*, Nature Park/Mark Boulton (pp. 34–5); *Impact Photos*, Cardboard City/Peter Arkell (p. 10); A Family in Bed and Breakfast Accommodation/David Reed (p. 10); *Leeds Leisure Services*, Temple Mills (p. 40), Interior of Temple Mills (p. 41); *London Transport Museum*, Golders Green (p. 12); *Manchester City Council Planning Department*, Chinese Imperial Arch (p. 39); *The Mansell Collection*, Drawing of Brighton Seaside Resort (pp. 32–3); *Marks and Spencer*, Logo (p. 25); *John Menzies*, Logo (p. 25); *Metrocentre*, Metroland Balloon and Lift (pp. 28–9); *Metropolitan Bradford Libraries*, Manningham Mills (pp. 40–41), General View, Bradford (p. 40); *The National Trust Photographic Library*, Medieval Clergy House/Rob Matheson (p. 14); *Nicholas Grimshaw & Partners Ltd*, Grand Union Walk Development (p. 16); *Peter Pedley*, Leek Market Place (p. 22); *Poggenpohl*, High Tech Kitchen (p. 18); *Jeremy Preston*, Byker Housing (p. 4); *Royal Commission on The Historical Monuments of England*, Hoover Building (pp. 40–41); *Royal National Theatre, London* (p. 38); *Selfridges*, Advertisement (pp. 24–5); *Pat Shirreff-Thomas*, The Forge, Glasgow (p. 29); *Spence and Webster Architects*, Milton Keynes Energy House (p. 21); *The Still Moving Picture Company*, Tourist Information Logo, (p. 32); *Tesco Creative Services*, Tesco Superstore, Hereford (p. 27); *The Board of Trustees of the Victoria and Albert Museum*, Van Asloot; The Triumph of Isabella (p. 38); *Virgin*, Logo (p. 24); *Elizabeth Whiting Associates*, Post Modern Interior (p. 19); City Traditional Interior (p. 19); *W H Smith*, Logo (p. 25); Wigan Pier, Brochure (p. 23); *Philip Wolmuth*, Killingworth Centre (p. 27).

Original artwork by:
Debbie Clark: pp. 2–3, p. 28;
Mark Dunn: p. 7 (top right), p. 8 (bottom), p. 12 (bottom), p. 18 (bottom right), p. 26 (top), p. 28 (top), p. 36 (left), p. 37 (left), p. 39, p. 43 (top);
Tim Hayward: p. 4, p. 4–5, p. 6 (top), pp. 6–7, p. 7 (top), p. 8 (3 at top), p. 11 (middle), p. 12 (middle), p. 18 (top and left), p. 20, p. 21 (top, right, middle), p. 22 (bottom), p. 25 (right), p. 26 (bottom), p. 27 (middle), p. 33 (right), p. 34 (bottom), p. 35 (3 on right), p. 37 (top right, bottom right), p. 40 (bottom), p. 45 (bottom);
Sarah Jowsey: p. 13 (middle), pp. 22–23 (top), p. 44 (top);
Mike Miller: p. 2 (bottom), p. 3 (middle), p. 11 (bottom), p. 27 (top), p. 31;
Liz Roberts: p. 20 (top), p. 44 (bottom);
Joshua Smith: p. 32 (bottom).

Every effort has been made to contact copyright holders and we apologise if any have been overlooked.